W9-CFO-873

6-6-2009

Always be proud of who you are!

Enjoy this 1st edition of Just Imagine —

Donnie J Kilburn, Jr

Just Imagine

A collection of 18 stories rich in values with loveable characters.

by
Bonnie Jean Kilburn, Jr.

Copyright 1998 by Bonnie Jean Kilburn, Jr.
P.O. Box 453
Newberry MI 49868

Illustrations by
Mary Frey

Library of Congress Card No. 98-94185
ISBN # 0-9668713-0-8

Printed in Michigan, U.S.A., by
Lake Superior Press
Marquette, Michigan 49855

No portion of this publication may be reproduced, reprinted or otherwise copied for distribution purposes without the express written permission from the author.

The Upper Peninsula of Michigan provides a beautiful setting for an author. It is said that one cannot go home again, but Bonnie has returned to the peaceful backdrop of the Upper Peninsula's Two Hearted and Tahquamenon Rivers, Lake Superior, and the forests which boast of maple, beech, and pine trees interwoven with a multitude of creatures. It is here that she finds the inspiration for her writings. She completed her Bachelor of Science degree at Northern Michigan University in Marquette, Michigan. Michigan State University awarded her a Master of Arts in Communication.

Bonnie's goal has been to write and speak. One must experience life to write and talk about it, and Bonnie has: student personnel at both NMU and MSU, a secondary education teacher with an elementary endorsement, a communication instructor at the University of Hawaii in Hilo, a real estate sales person, a photographer for Life Touch Photography Studios, an Emergency Medical Technician, the owner of Bons' Bon Bons (homemade candy business), and an insurance agent. Bonnie will tell you, "Each career was important, and I was thoroughly enriched by the people I met!"

She writes for enjoyment, but also out of concern. Some issues never go away. "If my writings touch a reader, then I have succeeded!"

Bonnie Kilburn photo by Cropshop/Richard King

Although she calls herself retired, Mary Frey continues to do freelance illustration for very special projects, such as this book of poems.

Her life-long career as an artist began after graduation from Northwestern University in Evanston, Illinois with a degree in art.

She worked for a package design studio in Chicago and as a graphic designer both freelance and full time for 17 years in Marquette for Lake Superior Press.

Mary and her husband, John, a retired chemistry professor at Northern Michigan University, have recently relocated to San Luis Obispo, California to be near their four children and four grandchildren, all residents of California.

There are special people in each of our lives who have helped us along our paths. In my life there have been many. I would like to acknowledge just a few. My devoted parents, Bonnie and Jim Kilburn, who taught me so much about life and nature and instilled a great deal of confidence in me! My special Aunt, Clairnell Douglas (Sis), who is an excellent example of laughter being the best medicine. Two exceptional teachers - Frances Flower (my 4th/5th grade teacher) and Genevieve Dwyer (my high school speech teacher) - both had a tremendous impact on my life. A wonderful friend, Betty J. Wescott, who has continuously encouraged me to publish my stories. Sue Schaefer, my very dear friend since childhood - I have the greatest admiration for her! And last, but far from least, three very special friends: Karen Reese, Darcy Toth, and Bob Carty.

My love and admiration go to each and every one of you. Thank you all for always being there!

Table of Contents

Star Gazer

Sometimes at night
when I can't sleep,
I cast my eyes
upon the heap
of stars that seem
to wink and peep
so distant
in the darkness deep.
They twinkle
and they glisten.
I observe
and then I listen.

The sight is like
an orchestra of sound.
I stand spellbound
and feast upon
the beauty that I see.
Perhaps this performance
was created just for me!
I see the constellations,
Aquarius and The Bear.
The sight has left me
speechless.

I sit and then I stare.
The Northern Lights
begin their dance.
They shimmer then they shake.
They illuminate the stage above
and keep me wide awake.
A shooting star from south to north
briefly leaves a trail.

Another one from east to west.
Its trail begins to pale.
I start counting all the stars above,
like a harvest that I'll reap.
Such peaceful mathematics!
I drift back off to sleep.

Clouds

I snatched a cloud down from the sky
and asked it all the reasons why
it liked to rain and block the sun
which did not seem like any fun
to me!

"Why, I love my job!" it seemed to shout.
"Just take a moment, look about."
"Everything that you can see
depends on little clouds like me!"

"The earth itself could not survive
and nothing here would be alive
were it not for clouds and rain we give
to all of earth so it may live."

"The roots of trees, each blade of grass,
the flower gardens that you pass,
each bird that flies, all moose that roam,
without a doubt would lose their home!"

"Perhaps you have a selfish view?
Are you thinking just of you?
It may seem the greatest fun
occurs on days when there is sun."

"If you take a moment and look toward the skies
the beauty of the clouds above will fill up both your eyes.
Their formations change so quickly, they swirl and move so fast.
They're here, then there, then gone again! They never seem to last!"

"They're soft and bright, so white they're stark,
then gray and black and days turn dark.
They open up and raindrops fall:
our gift to earth, to one and all."

"So, you see, we have our task
and this is all that we will ask:
When you see us passing by
remember there's a reason why."

I tossed the cloud back to the sky
and felt a tear moist in my eye.
Now every day I look above
and view each cloud I see with love!

Color Blind

Please!
Don't look at me through angry eyes.
I have nothing to disguise.
If my skin is all you see
then you're not
seeing all of me.

In nature there are colors-
greens and reds and blues.
All add brilliance to a world
so drab without these hues.

Does the blue sky think it's better
than the greens upon the earth?
Any gray mountains rising to the sky,
don't they have their worth?

Do you really think the white moon says,
"My color is supreme!"
Nature blends to make the crop.
No one color is the creme.

6

Do you recall selecting
the color that you'd be?
Or were you born the way you are?

The same is true for me.

So, please!
If my skin is all you see
remember…
you're not seeing all of me.

Timmm-ber!

The silence of the forest
was broken with a roar
when a maple tree,
whose time had come,
fell and stood no more.

It had occupied that very spot
for one hundred fifty years
and had gained the admiration
of all his nearby peers.

Trees, I know, communicate
in one form or another
and bonds are formed between them
like a sister or a brother.

So the absence of the maple
affected all the nearby trees.
You could hear the chatter everywhere
and the sadness in the breeze.

Those who knew the maple
reflected on his past
and through such conversation
his memory would last.

There was laughter mixed with sadness.
"Remember when" would bring a tear.
Then the silence of the forest
was all that they could hear.

It's so difficult to lose someone
who we hold so dear,
knowing we won't see them.
They will not again appear.

Except within our minds and hearts-
there they'll always live-
and when we seek their companionship
that's what our memories will give.

There's More to Me Than That

I'm a little flabby!
OK! Ok! I'm fat-
but even though there's a lot of me
there's more to me than that!

Why if I took my heart out
and placed it in my hand
you could see it beating
for peace throughout the land.

And if you looked into my eyes—
looked straight into my soul,
you could see that harmony
would be my final goal.

And if you listened to my thoughts
and forgot about my looks,
you'd discover new ideas
not found in any books.

Sure I'm a little heavy,
you might call me fat,
but turn me inside out
and see exactly where I'm at.

Just get beyond the outside
and contemplate what's in.
You'll see it really doesn't matter
being fat or being thin!

11

The Slick Dill Pickle

There was once a slick dill pickle,
floating in a jar.
When I tried to spear it,
it let out with a rar!!!
(that's picklish for roar)

I know this seems far-fetched,
so a picture I have sketched.
Just in case you see this pickle
doing back strokes in your jar!

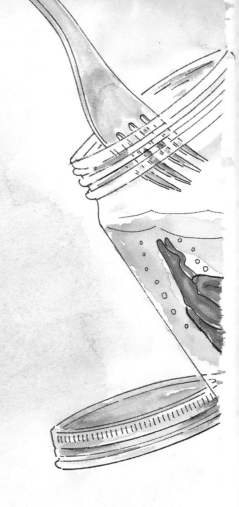

For you see, this pickle was a swimmer
who simply loved the salty scene,
in addition to the back stroke
it had a whole routine.

First the swan dive, then the back stroke,
under water for a while;
up for air and on its side,
then the side stroke for a mile.

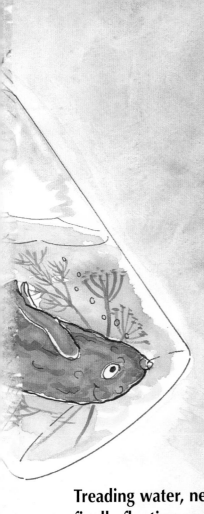

Treading water, next the breast stroke,
finally floating on its back;
Dive, dive, down to the bottom
when my fork went on the attack!

The pickle slithered to the left,
then bounded to the right!
I never knew a pickle
to put up such a fight!!

The duel went on for hours,
lasting way into the night!
The pickle was the victor,
so, I put the lid on tight!!

The Cardinal and the Blue Jay

At a local backyard feeder
on a white December day,
two birds flew in to feed awhile,
a cardinal and a jay.

Being leery of each other,
because of color I suppose,
whatever one would comment on
the other would oppose.

The bluejay broke the silence,
bluejays love to chat,
but the cardinal's sole response was,
"I don't agree with that!"

Their feelings toward each other
resulted from the past.
When generations don't forgive,
prejudice will last!

The cardinal had been cautioned
by family and by friends,
"You just can't trust a bluejay
so watch if one descends!"

So, not knowing any better,
the cardinal took his stance.
The bluejay offered friendship
but he really had no chance.

So the bluejay faced the cardinal
and this is what he said,
"You've no reason to dislike me
just because I am not red!"

When the cardinal thought about it,
not one reason he could find,
to act so rudely to this bird
and treat him so unkind.

15

Of course, it isn't easy
to admit when one is wrong.
So the silence grew between them
and lasted very long.

The cardinal thought of flying,
to avoid what he must do.
Instead, he faced the bluejay,
"I apologize to you."

When I saw you at the feeder,
I was not sure how I should act,
so I gave you the cold shoulder
based on hearsay, not on fact.

You've been more than friendly to me
it was nothing that you did.

I've heard tales about you bluejays
since I was just a kid!

That day the cardinal broke tradition
and offered friendship on the spot.
And to this day they're the best of friends,
all prejudice forgot!

Fishing Buddies

One sunny day in late July
I was fishing from my boat.
With rod in hand and worm on hook,
My bobber was afloat.

My bobber bobbed so gently
up and down each lapping wave,
the worm below bobbed with it,
so valiant and so brave.

A walleye slowly swam by,
eyeing up the bait,
knowing if she ate the worm
she would meet her fate.

So...the worm and fish
discussed a plan and took a course of action.
The trick, you see, was played on me!
Much to their satisfaction.

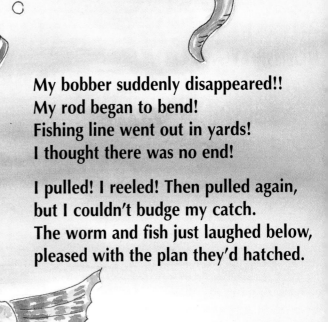

My bobber suddenly disappeared!!
My rod began to bend!
Fishing line went out in yards!
I thought there was no end!

I pulled! I reeled! Then pulled again,
but I couldn't budge my catch.
The worm and fish just laughed below,
pleased with the plan they'd hatched.

I thought my rod would surely break
or the line would snap in two!
What kind of fish could I have hooked?
I did not have a clue.

The battle that I undertook
seemed to last forever.
The scheme devised by worm and fish
was well planned out and clever.

Suddenly, the line was free,
my bobber back afloat.
I reeled in line and grabbed the hook-
attached to it this note:

"We wrapped your line around a log,
sat back and watched the action.
Several fish enjoyed the show!
You were the main attraction.

We know you'd like to catch us.
We can understand this wish.
Maybe you will! Maybe you won't!"

Sincerely, Worm and Fish

Stars in a Jar

The Big Dipper,
as a joke I think,
scooped up all the stars
and bottled them quite neatly
in one humongous jar!

I'm sure I need not tell you
that the stars were all quite shocked!
There they were, stuck in that jar,
with the lid securely locked.

The sight, of course, was dazzling!
Just imagine all those stars.
Their brightness lit the universe
from Mexico to Mars.

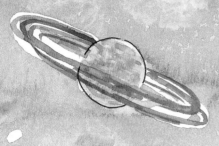

Despite their many efforts
the stars could not break out,
and I suspect they'd still be in that jar
except for what then came about!

The stars, you know, have been around
for a million years or more,
and when the dipper scooped them up that night
it shook the universe to the core.

The moon, known for its patience,
had silently watched this event,
but he felt he should speak to the dipper,
so this is the message he sent:

"My dear friend, Mr. Dipper,
my goodness, how busy you've been!
But I must ask you this question,
Will you put the stars back, and just when?"

"You see...There are millions
who look to the heavens
who love the peaceful darkness at night.
This prank that you've pulled is an interesting one.
Did you realize it would cause such a sight?"

Upon reading the note, the Big Dipper
suddenly realized just what he had done.
It was purely a prank, for something to do,
but it had gone far beyond having fun!

How quickly the dipper took action.
He loosened, then opened the lid.
He tipped the jar over and shook it
and out of the jar each star slid.

Each star took its place in the heavens
and the Big Dipper had to agree.
This beauty should be shared by everyone
it was truly a sight all should see!

The Sunfish

With just one wish
I'd be a fish
and swim out to the sea.
No whale or shark or octopus
would ever frighten me.
I think I'd be a sunfish
with an array of colors true-
oranges and greens and yellows
all mixed with powder blue.
I'd dazzle fish around me,
their fins would point my way,
schools would pause and chatter
and you would hear them say,
"That sunfish is so striking,
like a rainbow passing by!"

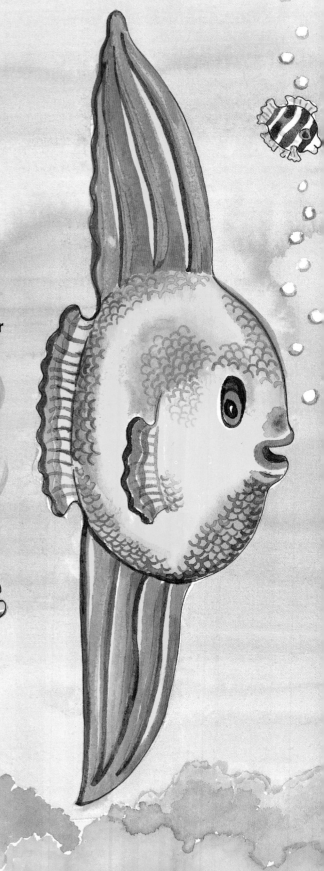

24

They would stop my journey
and then they'd ask me "Why?"
"Why were you so lucky
to have beauty since your birth?"
In honesty I'd answer,
"That says nothing of my worth!"
All you fish around me
have beauty of your own
just look within and you will find
that I am not alone.
Swim proudly as you journey on.
These words I tell you true,
"You have no say in who you are,
you are simply you.
Love yourself for who you are,
beautiful or not.
Think good thoughts about yourself,
You are who you've got!"

Slow Down

I was moving at a snail's pace,
of course I am a snail,
when a hot shot clam sped by me
and left me in its trail.

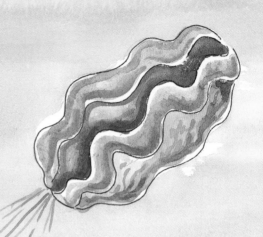

The stirred up sand was all I saw
so I ducked into my shell
and stayed there for awhile
to let the bottom quell.

Then I started on my way again
when an urchin passed me by
and the spiny little rascal
was really on the fly!

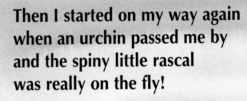

"Got to pass you! In a hurry!
My destination calls to me!"
Once again the sand was riled
and of course I could not see.

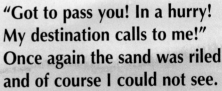

So back into my shell I went
where I had a little lunch,
some salty grains of bottom sand
and tasty ocean punch.

With my journey underway again
I was stopped dead in my tracks.
An Octopus, all legs of course, yelled,
"Your pace is far too lax!"

"Get a move on! Speed it up!
You move so doggone slow!"
To which my calm response was,
"Where do I have to go?"

I am really teased quite often
about the slowness of my pace.
To this I always answer,
"Life is not a race!"

I may not be the first one
to arrive at any spot,
But besides the shell upon my back
time is all I've got!

Sometimes, for entertainment,
I stop and park my shell.
Then I watch as life goes by me.
Oh, the stories I could tell!

There's dodging and there's darting
and veering in and out!
So many in a hurry!
They yell and often shout.

So many are impatient
and tempers often flare.
I'll make one small suggestion,
if I even dare!

Slow Down!

Your destination will await you
so relax and take your time.
You may get teased a little,
but going slow is not a crime!

The Lady in the Moon

There's a lady in the moon, you know,
who has held her portrait pose
for one hundred fifty thousand years
or longer I suppose.

Her head is somewhat tilted
like a locket cameo.
She models for the universe,
well poised, just like a pro.

She never seems to tire
of the crowds she entertains,
and the weather is no bother,
even when it rains.

It takes a special lady
to fulfill this job request:
well poised with perfect posture
and gracious as a guest.

So cast your eyes upon the moon
and you'll see the lady there.
She's on the stage most every night
with a performance, oh so rare!

Ever Have a Toothache?

While strolling on the beaches
of the sun swept balmy south,
I happened on a great white shark
who opened up his mouth.

He motioned for my presence
and as I cautiously drew near,
with his fin he pointed to a tooth
located near the rear.

My first reaction was to look,
just stick my head inside.
The shark seemed all too eager
and he opened up more wide.

Of course I gained my senses.
I stepped back and then I said,
"You almost tricked me, Mr. Shark!
I almost lost my head!"

But when I looked into his eyes
there was a pleading sort of glance,
so I mustered up the courage
and decided to take a chance.

I proceeded still with caution
and said, "Let me look from here."
So he held his mouth wide open
and what I saw confirmed my fear.

A toothache is a terrible thing.
It makes you want to scream.
I've tried all remedies I can find
from gels, to oils, to creams.

Of course, extraction is one method.
Just pull the tooth right out!
And when I saw the pain this shark was in
it left me with no doubt!

"Ah, I see you have a toothache."
The shark nodded to agree.
"I think I'll have to take the tooth
then send you back to sea."

I suppose the bravest of all creatures
is afraid from time to time.
The shark proved no exception
as his fears began to climb.

I consoled him with the words I'd heard,
"There won't be any pain."
Then I told him what we'd have to do
and hoped he would remain.

I would have to act quite quickly
so I found some fishing line.
I tied it to the ailing tooth
and said I'd count to nine.

After counting up to number nine
I took off on a run.
I felt a tug, than something snapped.
I hoped the job was done.

I ran back to the ocean
to check on my success
I'd never pulled a tooth before
so I was scared, I must confess.

The fishing line lay in the sand
and then I found the end.
I showed the shark the dangling tooth.
He looked my way and grinned.

The salty water in the sea
helps cuts and bruises heal,
so I told the shark to gargle
and delay his evening meal.

Before he swam away that day
in his own majestic style,
he turned my way to thank me
with a minus-one-tooth smile!

The Polar Bear in Underwear

In a region of the Arctic,
where the air is very cold,
one polar bear wears underwear.
A move which is quite bold!

You can see him in his longjohns
across the distant miles,
and no matter where he strolls about,
his appearance brings forth smiles!

Of course, the first time he was spotted
in his bright red underwear
everybody laughed out loud,
but he simply did not care.

"The reason for my longjohns,"
he announced to those close by,
"Is because I'm cold most all the time.
That's the reason why!"

It took some getting used to,
this sight which was so rare,
after all, it was a first,
longjohns on a bear!

When he looks into calm waters
where his reflection he can see,
if any bear is standing near
he proudly says, "That's me!"

So everyone respects him.
He is different, it is true,

and sometimes being different
is hard for me and you.

To my knowledge, throughout history,
there's been no other bear
that's been spotted in the Arctic
wearing bright red underwear!

It's said that to this very day
he wanders back and forth.
The only bear in underwear
way up in the north!

The Wise Old Tree

I was resting in the forest
with my back against a tree
when the tree began to whisper
"Listen, please to me."

I'm sure you think we stand here
unaware of life around,
but let me set you straight on this...
Life's secrets we have found.

We've watched the seasons come and go,
seen dark turn into light;
we've been warmed by days of sunshine
then cooled by evening night.

We've stood here as the hands of time
have circled round and round.
The young new leaves come out in spring,
in fall they drift to ground.

We've watched as children climb each branch,
reaching high towards the sky,
the birds have nestled in our limbs,
where their young have learned to fly.

We've watched young lovers stroll along,
then kiss beneath our shade,
their love remains among us,
even when their shadows fade.

We've watched the aged slowly stroll,
giving thanks for all we've done.
They know that we'll remain here
long after they have gone.

We've learned patience as we've stood here,
and we wish we could impart
the wisdom that we now possess.
Observations from the heart.

Each day for us brings something new,
whether rain or sun prevails.
I could talk for hours
and tell a thousand tales.

But in silence we continue
to stand here and observe.
Patience is our virtue,
we're simply here to serve.

The Sunbather

I was sitting on a log one day,
the sun warm upon my shell.
When two humans paddled by me
and broke my sleepy spell!

I poked my head out,
looked around and thought,
"Here we go again,"
with net in hand and eye on me,
their faces wore a grin!

Don't ask me why
But humans love to try
and capture me.
I stay positioned on my log,
Ignoring them's the key!!

"Look! A giant tortoise!"
I look around to see.
No giant tortoise anywhere,
but they're looking straight at me!

I look into the water,
my reflection I can see,
I'm not a giant tortoise,
I'm just little bitty me!

I suppose it's like those fish tales
where the big one got away.
The "big one" was a minnow
but that's not for me to say!

Sometimes humans paddle on
and leave well enough alone,
but today is not my lucky day,
I can feel it in my bone!

It's said we turtles move so slow,
that we're such an easy catch.
When humans tower over us
they think we are no match!

But sunning on a log each day
gives me plenty time to think
and by the time the net swerves
towards me--
I've slipped into the drink!

I Am Simply Me!

While walking through the woods one day,
I heard the rustling leaves.
I looked around and saw, at least,
a thousand different trees!

A maple tree began to speak
and talked about its leaves,
how all the colors magnify,
they mix and interweave.

"My sap runs sweet in springtime,
and to heaven I do reach,
but I cannot help but wonder
if I'd rather be a beech!"

Now close at hand, just fifteen feet,
a beech tree proudly grew,
"Listen, Maple, while I speak,
these words I tell you true."

"I've given thought to other trees,
I've observed the towering pine,
I've watched the willow and the oak
but was proud of what was mine!"

"I may not be the tallest,
or the grandest of us trees,
but I have learned to listen
to the wisdom in the breeze."

"All of us, at one time,
have thought about our plot.
We've looked around and pondered
what the other trees have got."

Some are tall and graceful,
some are short and fat,
and I, like you, have thought at times,
"I'd rather be like that!"

"But then I stop and think
about how thankful I should be,
and I grow grander with the thought
that I AM SIMPLY ME!"

41

Pass It On

I gave a smile to a friend
hoping that this friend would send
the smile to another friend
who would send it on its way.
Thus my smile would continue on
and know no end this day.
A smile you know,
passed to and fro,
can warm the soul
from head to toe.
It can turn a frown around
and lift your feet
up off the ground.
So give a friend a smile.
Then sit back and wait and see.
This smile will travel everywhere
and then come back to me.